HÄGAR

in a fix

℞
RAVETTE BOOKS

This edition first published by Ravette Books Limited 1991

Printed and Bound
for Ravette Books Limited,
3 Glenside Estate, Star Road, Partridge Green,
Horsham, West Sussex RH13 8RA
An Egmont Company,
by Cox & Wyman Ltd, Reading

ISBN: 1 85304 313 3

HAMLET   LUCKY EDDIE   HÄGAR   HELGA   SNERT   HONI

SVEN SVENSON IS THE MAN FOR ME...HE'S NICE... HE'S HANDSOME ...HE'S SMART...HE'S HARD WORKING...

HE'S FUNNY... HE'S STRONG, HE'S KIND...

HE'S MARRIED

EVERYBODY HAS A FEW LITTLE FLAWS...

DIK BROWNE